NOT TO BE TAKEN
Seriously

Other books by Colin West:

Out of the Blue from Nowhere
Back to Front and Back Again
Winslow and his Bathtub

(Published by Dennis Dobson)

NOT TO BE TAKEN

Seriously

POEMS & PICTURES BY
COLIN WEST

Hutchinson
London Melbourne Sydney Auckland Johannesburg

Hutchinson & Co. (Publishers) Ltd

An imprint of the Hutchinson Publishing Group

17-21 Conway Street, London W1P 5HL

Hutchinson Group (Australia) Pty Ltd
30-32 Cremorne Street, Richmond South, Victoria 3121
PO Box 151, Broadway, New South Wales 2007

Hutchinson Group (NZ) Ltd
32-34 View Road, PO Box 40-086, Glenfield, Auckland 10

Hutchinson Group (SA) (Pty) Ltd
PO Box 337, Bergvlei 2012, South Africa

First published 1982

© Colin West 1982

Set in Plantin by Bookens, Saffron Walden, Essex

Printed in Great Britain by The Anchor Press Ltd
and bound by Wm Brendon & Son Ltd,
both of Tiptree, Essex

British Library Cataloguing in Publication Data
Colin, West
    Not to be taken seriously.
    I. Title
    823'.914[J]   PZ7

ISBN 0 09 147180 X

CONTENTS

SOME OF MY WORST FRIENDS

Adolphus

Adolphus is despicable –
Before the day begins,
To prove that I am kickable,
He kicks me in the shins.

Norman Norton's Nostrils

Oh, Norman Norton's nostrils
Are powerful and strong;
Hold on to your belongings
If he should come along.

And do not ever let him
Inhale with all his might,
Or else your pens and pencils
Will disappear from sight.

Right up his nose they'll vanish;
Your future will be black.
Unless he gets the sneezes,
You'll *never* get them back!

Nicola

I'm glad I'm not
Like Nicola,
Who may look sweet
As honey.
But even if you
Tickle her,
She doesn't find
It funny.

Wilhelmina

Were she leaner,
Wilhelmina
Could have been a
Ballerina.

She'd the vigour,
But her figure
Just got bigger
And BIGGER
And BIGGER!

Humphrey Hughes of Highbury

Young Humphrey Hughes of Highbury
Goes to his local library;
They stamp his books, he softly speaks,
'I'll bring them back within three weeks.'
He always looks so meek and mild
That grown-ups think, 'There goes a child
Who'll grow into a charming youth.'
But little do they know the truth.

For when he's home, young Humphrey Hughes
Forgets to ever wipe his shoes,
And at his mother merely sneers
As to his room he disappears.
When there his library books he takes,
His body with excitement shakes,
For Humphrey so enjoys himself
When placing books upon his shelf.

But there upon his shelf they stay,
Untouched, unread, until the day
He takes one down and with a grin
Looks at the date that's stamped within.
With laughter he begins to shriek,
For all his books were due last week.
He then decides the thing to do
Is wait another week or two.

So time goes by until, at last,
When six or seven weeks have passed,

There comes the knock upon the door
That Humphrey has been waiting for.
His mother gets a nasty shock
When answering the caller's knock,
For there she finds two boys in blue –
In search of books long overdue.

But, pleading absentmindedness,
Young Hughes could simply not care less,
And so, with some reluctancy,
The constables accept his plea.
They take the long-lost books away,
But warn he'll have a fine to pay,
Yet Humphrey merely looks benign,
For Mummy always pays the fine!

The Dreadful Duo

Against my better judgement I've
Asked Jack and Jill to tea.
They said they'd come at half past five,
But whensoever they arrive
Will be too soon for me.

If you don't know these dreadful twins,
I'll tell you what they do:
They box your ears and kick your shins
And throw down their banana skins
As though you asked them to.

They never leave till nearly ten,
And when at last they go,
They say they'd like to come again,
And ask if you can tell them when,
To which you must say 'No!'

Nora the Nibbler

Nora nibbles like a rabbit,
It's a funny sort of habit.
First a carrot she will pick up,
Nibble it, then start to hiccup,
After which she'll start to nibble
Once more at her vegetibble.

Winifred

Why do you do it,
Winifred?
Why do you stand
Upon your head?
Why don't you stand
Upon your feet,
Like everybody
Else I meet?
Does standing up
That way instead
Ensure you keep
A level head?
Is *that* the reason,
Winifred?

15

My Obnoxious Brother Bobby

My obnoxious brother Bobby
Has a most revolting hobby;
There, behind the garden wall is
Where he captures creepy-crawlies.

Grannies, aunts and baby cousins
Come to our house in their dozens,
But they disappear discreetly
When they see him smiling sweetly.

For they know, as he approaches,
In his pockets are cockroaches,
Spiders, centipedes and suchlike;
All of which they do not much like.

As they head towards the lobby,
Bidding fond farewells to Bobby,
How they wish he'd change his habits
And keep guinea pigs or rabbits.

But their wishes are quite futile,
For he thinks that bugs are cute. I'll
Finish now, but just remind you:
Bobby could be right behind you!

Veronica

Whenever Veronica
Plays her harmonica,
She makes such a hideous row
That, seeking a proper tune,
The moment seems opportune
To visit a faraway cow.

Clumsy Clarissa

Clarissa did the washing up:
She smashed a plate and chipped a cup,
And dropped a glass and cracked a mug,
Then pulled the handle off a jug.
She couldn't do much worse, you'd think,
But then she went and broke the sink.

When Susan Sings

When Susan sings
She causes
My eyes to fill
With tears.
But when she stops
Or pauses,
It's music to
My ears!

Big Jim

When we play cricket, we don't let Jim bowl;
And when we play baseball, we don't let Jim bat.
But when we play football, we put Jim in goal,
For balls can't get past him, because Jim's so fat.

My Brother's Violin

Behold the battered violin
That's tucked beneath my brother's chin.
He has no bow, so has to pluck
The strings. It's really rotten luck.
So why the smile upon his face,
As though the world's a sunny place?
What does he find that's so hilarious?
He thinks he's got a Stradivarius.

Wilma's Wig

Wilma's wig is much too big
And when she puts it on,
People stare and wonder where
On earth she might have gone.

Tiny Tony and His Pony

Tiny Tony had a pony,
He fed it tea and cakes.
Brother Brian had a lion,
He fed it juicy steaks.

Tiny Tony rode his pony
To the local park.
Brother Brian and his lion
Followed after dark.

Tiny Tony and his pony
Vanished without trace.
Brother Brian and his lion
Licked each other's face.

UN-NATURAL HISTORY

The Grumblegrug

It's slippery and slimy,
It slithers like a slug.
It's gruesome and it's grimy,
It's called the Grumblegrug.

Along the gutter crawling
It likes to go at night.
Its habits are appalling;
It's not a pretty sight.

But should you ever spot one,
Don't squash it needlessly,
But just be glad you're *not* one,
A Grumblegrug like me.

The Flipper-Flopper Bird

O have you never ever heard
Of the Flipper-Flopper Bird?
O have you never seen his teeth,
Two above and one beneath?

O have you never known the thrill
Of stroking his enormous bill?
O have you never taken tea
With him sitting up a tree?

O have you never seen him hop
As he goes a-flip, a-flop?
O have you never heard his cry?
No, you've never? Nor have I.

The Ogglewop

The Ogglewop is tall and wide,
And though he looks quite passive,
He's crammed with boys and girls inside,
— That's why he is so massive!

The Lolloping Lollop

The Lolloping Lollop
Will meet you one morning,
And give you a wallop
Without any warning.
It's destined to happen,
There's no need to doubt it,
But don't be concerned
And don't worry about it.
For Lolloping Lollops
Have one saving virtue,
They all say they're sorry
Soon after they've hurt you.

The Thinkalot

Of all the things I'm glad I'm not
There's one thing in particular –
I'm glad I'm not a Thinkalot
Or *Pondus perpendicular.*

The Thinkalot can stand up straight,
His head is almost spherical,
But vain attempts to find a mate
Have driven him hysterical.

He gabbles at the first excuse
And seems quite intellectual,
But is, in fact, of little use,
His brain is ineffectual.

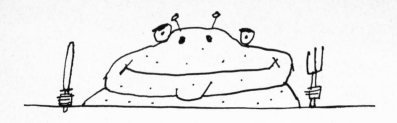

The Finisher-Upper

To demolish a dinner
Or diminish a supper,
Why don't you call for
The Finisher-Upper?

Watch him demolish
And watch him diminish
Any old left-over food
He can finish.

His performance is always
So perfect and polished:
Suppers diminished
And dinners demolished!

The Glump

Your life may be in jeopardy,
The Glump is on its way.
Its legs are long and leopardy,
It pounces on its prey.

It bears some similarity,
You'll notice, to a bird.
Its beak is pink and parroty,
Its cry is quite absurd.

I think the Glump is easily
Our most obnoxious beast.
Its teeth are white and weasely,
And waiting for a feast.

You'll reel and writhe in agony,
Unless you disappear.
Its skin is dry and dragony . . .
Oh dear, the Glump is here.

27

The Neither-One-Thing-Nor-Another

The Neither-One-Thing-Nor-Another
Is neither round nor square,
Has neither hide nor hair,
Can neither do nor dare.

The Neither-One-Thing-Nor-Another
Is neither foul nor fair,
Goes neither dressed nor bare,
Can neither growl nor glare.

The Neither-One-Thing-Nor-Another
Has gone to Who-Knows-Where,
But no one seems to care,
It's neither here nor there.

HYSTERICAL CHARACTERS

Adam and Eve

Said Adam to Eve, 'I wonder if we've
Got time for a seven-course luncheon.'
But Eve shook her head and offered instead
A solitary apple to munch on.

29

Pythagoras

With no hesitation
Pythagoras the Greek
Could solve an equation
That would take me a week!

Archimedes

When Archimedes cried 'Eureka!'
And leapt out of his bath,
The people sighed, 'Another streaker!'
And kept out of his path.

Diogenes

Diogenes was cynical
And lived inside a tub.
He wasn't clean or clinical,
And seldom did he scrub.

He felt no need to wander off
Or visit anyone,
But once told Alexander off
For blocking out the sun.

Ancient Greeks

Sophocles and Socrates,
Euclid and Euripides,
Homer and Hippocrates;
Ancient Greeks were all of these.

Alfred the Great

Alfred the Great was a hero,
But heroes can still make mistakes.
He didn't watch fires like Nero,
And ended up burning the cakes.

Raleigh and Elizabeth

When Raleigh met Elizabeth,
And it was rather muddy,
He wouldn't let her feet get wet,
He *was* a fuddy-duddy.

So he laid down his velvet cloak,
The Queen, she didn't falter.
She thought it odd, but on it trod,
And said, 'Arise, Sir Walter.'

Napoleon

Napoleon Bonaparte
Was never alone, apart
From when he'd tell his queen:
'Not tonight, Josephine.'

Charles Blondin

Do you think that Charles Blondin
Practised over a pond in
Preparing to stagger a-
 cross Niagara?

Sir Isaac Newton

Sir Isaac Newton liked to grapple
With problems astronomical.
Then on his head there fell an apple,
Which may strike you as comical.
But for Sir Isaac 'twas to be
A matter of some gravity.

James Watt

Whenever James Watt
Felt fit to scream,
His head became hot
And he'd let off some steam.

Queen Victoria

Although Queen Victoria
Grew sadder and sorrier
When Albert did not prove immortal,
She was wrongly accused
Of not being amused,
For often she liked a good chortle.

DOTTY DITTIES

Alphonso

Alphonso went upon the stage
To be a famous actor,
But couldn't earn a steady wage,
So now he drives a tractor.

Tuba

The tuba is an instrument
That takes a lot of puff.
I tried to blow a tuba once,
But didn't have enough.

Blowing My Trumpet

I like to paddle my own canoe;
I hate to blow my trumpet.
But whatsoever I may do,
I like it or I lump it.

I'm Waiting for Nothing

I'm waiting for nothing to happen,
I'm waiting for no one to call,
I'm waiting for nowhere to go to,
So why am I waiting at all!

Because It Was There

One of the very cleverest
Of men who conquered Everest
Gave this reply when questioned why:
'Because it was there.'

I hope that this example shows
Just why I punched you on the nose.
If questioned why I shall reply:
'******* ** *** *****.'

Mona Lisa

I have so wondered for a while
What makes the Mona Lisa smile?
What fills her heart so full of cheer?
I'll ask the Laughing Cavalier!

A Pelican in Delhi Can

A pelican in Delhi can
Spend his whole life alone.
But an elephant in Delhi can't
Be often on his own.

Amongst My Friends

Amongst my friends
I number some
Sixteen or so
Who dance.
Some like to do
The rhumba, some
Will waltz if they've
The chance;
And even in
Their slumber, some
Will foxtrot in
A trance.
But as for me,
I'm cumbersome,
And all I do
Is prance.

My Dear, It's Delightful

My dear, it's delightful;
My dear, it's divine.
My dear, I adore it;
I wish it were mine.

My dear, I must get one,
No time to be lost.
But tell me, how much
Does an elephant cost?

The Ghost's Lament

'Hello' is what you used to say,
You said it most politely;
But now you look the other way,
As though I were unsightly.

Rain

Into each life some rain must fall,
The truth of this is painful;
For some have hardly none at all,
While some have endless rainfall.

Natalie

It isn't normal, Natalie,
Although you do it daily.
You dress up very tattily
And play the ukelele.

Yet once you dressed so nattily,
Oh Natalie, it's true.
Yes, once you dressed so nattily,
But now you never do.

Luke

Luke's a lisper.
I've heard a whisper,
He's at his zenith
Playing tennith.

Cucumber, Cucumber

Cucumber, cucumber,
Inside my wheelbarrow,
If you weren't so narrow
You'd look like a marrow.

Bed of Nails

I sleep upon a bed of nails.
I must confess it never fails
To help me get a good night's rest,
And, overall, I'm most impressed!

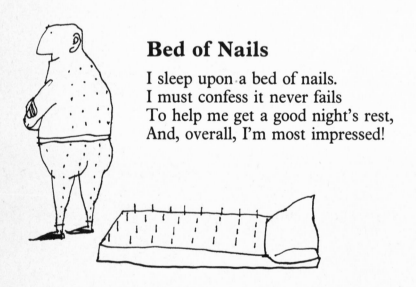

Kate

In the kitchen
Kate went tripping,
Landing in a
Vat of dripping.
When the Red Cross
Came to fetch her,
Kate kept slipping
Off the stretcher.

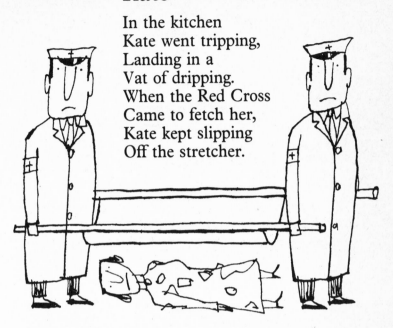

Uncle Fred

My Uncle Fred,
He went to bed,
He went to sleep
And dreamt he
Drank from a cup –
And waking up,
The goldfish bowl
Was empty.

My Sister Sybil

Sipping soup, my sister Sybil
Seems inclined to drool and dribble.
If it wasn't for this foible,
Meal-times would be more enjoyable!

When Betty Eats Spaghetti

When Betty eats spaghetti,
She slurps, she slurps, she slurps.
And when she's finished slurping,
She burps, she burps, she burps.

Advice

Please never put
Into your mouth
Those things which are
Inedible.
To suck a thumb
Is bad enough;
To suck a toe's
Incredible!

The Hole Truth

If it takes three men to dig one hole
Two hours and one minute,
How long would six men take to dig
A hole exactly twice as big,
And could you push them in it?

Six Tongue Twisters

I took a proper copper kettle
To the top of Popocatepetl.
And on the top of Popocatepetl
I put my proper copper kettle.

Cynthia Smith has still not thought
A single thought since Thursday,
Since Cynthia Smith is not the sort
To think a single sort of thought.

I want to be a wallaby,
A wallaby like Willoughby.
When *will* I be a wallaby
Like Willoughby the wallaby?

Herbert likes Hubert
And Hubert likes Schubert,
And Schubert liked sherbert
Like Hubert likes Herbert.

When Jilly eats jelly,
Then Jilly is jolly.
But melons make Melanie
Most melancholy.

Did Kitty wake
The kittiwake,
Or did the kittiwake
Wake Kitty?

Auntie Agnes's Cat

My Auntie Agnes has a cat.
I do not like to tell her that
Its body seems a little large
(With lots of stripes for camouflage).
Its teeth and claws are also larger
Than they ought to be. A rajah
Gave her the kitten, I recall,
When she was stationed in Bengal.
But that was many years ago,
And kittens are inclined to grow.
So now she has a fearsome cat –
But I don't like to tell her that.

MORALS AND MANNERS

The Trouble with Boys

The trouble with boys is
They make funny noises;
They rage and they riot,
And seldom are quiet.
They seem extra naughty
With folk over forty,
And do things they oughtn't
To persons important.

The Avaricious Boy

'Oh, see the sun above us shine,
I often wish it could be mine!'
Thus spoke the avaricious boy,
As though the sun were but a toy.
Explained his mother straightaway,
'The sun is not a thing of play,
And if this orb for which you yearn
Were given you, your hands would burn.
Far better we should wish for that
Which hurts us not – a ball to bat,
A kite to fly, a top to spin,
Or tiny soldiers made of tin.'
At this the avaricious boy
Commenced to clap and jump for joy,
And squealed, 'Mamma, the truth to tell,
I wish for all of those as well!'

Percy and the Python

Poor Percy met a python once
When walking in the jungle,
And being something of a dunce,
He made a fatal bungle.

He went to stroke its scaly skin
As from a tree it dangled.
Alas, before he could begin,
The python left him strangled.

It then went on to crush to pulp
His body, very neatly;
Until, with one enormous gulp,
It swallowed him completely.

This story shows that such a snake
Should always be avoided.
So do not make the same mistake
As this unthinking boy did!

Belated Bernie

As Maud and Mary walked to school,
Maud said unto the other,
'I fear we must the title "fool"
Bestow upon my brother.

For Bernard is an idle boy
Whose mischief drives me frantic.
His time he seems but to employ
In planning some new antic.

Just yesterday he "cut his thumb"
Whilst serving up the mutton.
The sight of blood quite struck him dumb –
I summoned Doctor Dutton.

Then Bernie, full of mirth, did bawl
(I wish they'd lock the wretch up),
You see, it wasn't blood at all,
But just tomato ketchup.'

'Your brother is a fool indeed,'
Reciprocated Mary.
'In future, of his tricks take heed;
Of false alarms be wary.'

Then as upon their way they went,
Their homework to deliver,
The air by frightful screams was rent.
They raced down to the river.

Maud found beyond the river bank
Her brother who was drowning,
But sighed, 'Aha, another prank!
No more I'll take your clowning.'

And thus she left him to his fate,
Continuing her journey.
At school she was a little late –
But not as late as Bernie.

The Greedy Alligator

I have a rather greedy pet,
A little alligator;
When he my younger sister met,
He opened wide and ate her.

But soon he learned that he was wrong
To eat the child in question,
For he felt bad before too long,
And suffered indigestion.

This story seems to prove to me
That he who rudely gobbles
Will soon regret his gluttony
And get the collywobbles.

The Painful Way to Multiply

The teacher viewed the infant boy
Without the slightest sense of joy,
For still he could not calculate
The simple sum of six times eight.

The teacher ranted angrily,
Then took the lad across his knee
And vowed to teach him with a cane
The way to multiply, with pain.

He gave the boy
   six of the best,
But would not let
   the matter rest,
And beat him six times
   more and then
He beat him six times
   once again.

And thus, in multiples
   of six,
Between the pupil's
   cries and kicks,
The teacher could well
   demonstrate
That six times eight
   is forty-eight.

The Vandal

See the vandal
Work the handle
Of the pump
At such a rate
That the water
Soaks the daughter
Of a local
Magistrate.

See the vandal, steeped in scandal,
Languishing both night and day.
Now imprisoned, weak and wizened,
He must for his mischief pay!

TOOTH AND CLAW

The Pig

The table manners of the pig
Leave much to be desired.
His appetite is always big,
His talk is uninspired.

And if you ask him out to dine
You'll only ask him once,
Unless you like to see a swine
Who gobbles as he grunts.

The Aardvark

O, the aardvark always comes in first
In any dictionary.
He may be slow and cumbersome,
But still we should be wary,
For he beats the lion and leopard,
And beats the dromedary;
He even beats the antelope,
It's most extraordinary!
I'd like to serenade him more,
But is it necessary
When the aardvark always comes in first
In any dictionary!

Proboscis Monkey

Proboscis monkey, I suppose
You've grown accustomed to your nose.
But what precisely did you do
To get that nose to grow on you?

The Barbary Sheep

The Barbary sheep,
It seems to me,
A hundred fleas
May harbour.
The Barbary sheep,
It's plain to see,
Has *never* seen
A barber!

The Oyster

The oyster, he is
Quite extraordinary:
The moister he is,
The more he is merry.

Chameleons

Chameleons are seldom seen,
They're red, they're orange, then they're green.
They're one of nature's strangest sights,
Their colours change like traffic lights!

Pangolin

This disrespectful pangolin
Reclines upon a pillow,
And plays upon a mandolin
Made from an armadillo.

To sing his songs is his intent,
At nineteen to the dozen,
And so he strums an instrument
That used to be his cousin.

The Polar Bear

In Arctic lands the polar bear
Is anything but svelte.
He lies about throughout the year,
And only has one nagging fear:
He hopes the sun will not appear
In case the ice should melt.

The Sea-lion

There's nothing feline about the sea-lion,
You'll notice if you meet one.
In fact, the sea-lion is more like sirloin,
You'll notice if you eat one.

The Sloth

The sloth may smile,
The sloth may frown.
It's hard to tell –
 he's upside-down!

The Rhinoceros

Abbreviate *linoleum* to *lino*,
And nobody will mind it in the least.
But shorten a *rhinoceros* to *rhino*
And you are bound to aggravate the beast.

The Crab

The crab has still far to evolve
Till he attains perfection,
For still, it seems, he cannot solve
The question of direction.
So when he goes from 'A' to 'B'
Along the ocean tideways,
He also visits 'C' and 'D',
Because he travels sideways!

The Wasp and Bumble-bee

Between the wasp and bumble-bee
There seems much similarity;
But bumble-bees will buzz for free,
Whilst wasps won't work for charity.

Glow-worm

I know a worried glow-worm,
I wonder what the matter is?
He seems so glum and gloomy,
Perhaps he needs new batteries!

Our Hippopotamus

We thought a lively pet to keep
Might be a hippopotamus.
Now see him sitting in a heap,
And notice at the bottom—us.

The Bat

The bat in flight at dead of night
Can flap about with ease,
For with his ears he somehow steers
A path between the trees.

Flamingoes

Flamingoes are a shocking pink,
With just one leg to stand on.
The other leg they use, I think,
To practise how to land on.

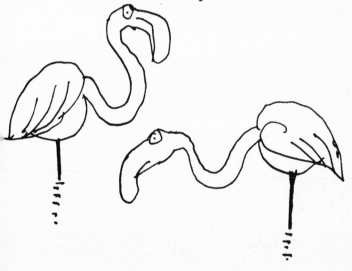

The Auk

How very awkward for the auk
To be resigned to merely squawk,
And never say a single word
To anyone but fellow bird.

And yet, supposing we could teach
The auk the art of human speech,
If we should ever ask him out,
Whatever would we talk about?

VICIOUS VERSES

Beryl

In her frock so gaily patterned
Beryl by a bus was flattened.
And the damage was extensive –
Oh, that dress was *so* expensive.

Burly Basil

Burly Basil was the victim
Of a bully rough and ruthless.
First the bully punched and kicked him,
Then he left poor Basil toothless.

Who'd have thought that burly Basil
(He who studied unarmed combat)
Would be beaten to a frazzle –
By a weedy-looking wombat?

Betty

Wearing all her diamonds, Betty
Rode too fast along the jetty.
How I wish she'd not been reckless;
We could not retrieve her necklace.

Bessie

As she worked the mangle, Bessie
Came unto an end most messy.
With the wash she got entangled,
Now she lies completely mangled.

Henry

When Henry from his ladder fell,
And broke his arm, and leg as well,
His wife was naturally upset –
He hadn't cleaned the windows yet.

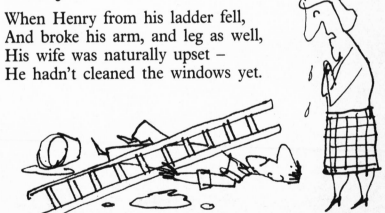

Eve

If I'd *known* Eve,
I'd have told her
Of that fast
Descending boulder.
But as she was
Just a stranger,
It seemed wrong
To mention danger.

Little Barbara

Little Barbara went to Scarborough,
Just to buy a candelabra.
At the harbour a bear ate Barbara.
Don't you find that most macabre?

Florence

Florence fell into the ocean,
And caused such a grand commotion
That if I were any braver
I'd have been inclined to save her.

Trevor

Fooling with a chopper, Trevor
Managed his own head to sever,
And to somehow calmly catch it –
Just before he dropped the hatchet.

Kitty

Isn't it a
Dreadful pity
What became of
Dreamy Kitty,
Noticing the
Moon above her,
Not
  the
    missing
      man-hole
        cover?

76

Laurence

Laurence by a lion was mauled,
And it's left us quite appalled.
He had on his 'Sunday best';
Now he's gone and torn his vest.

Wendy

Wendy went to gather sticks and
Sank up to her neck in quicksand.
How can fate be quite that cruel?
Now we have no winter fuel.

Polly and Pongo

When Polly and Pongo
Were lost in the Congo
And hadn't a morsel to eat,
The former got fatter
By eating the latter,
But didn't delight in the feat.

Freddy

Freddy down the
Mountain skiing
Hit and killed a
Human being;
And to top this
Sad disaster,
Had to have his
Toe in plaster.

Samantha

In the jungle skipped Samantha,
For her troubles to forget,
When she met a hungry panther
Who'd not had his breakfast yet.

But Samantha had some flowers,
So she gave the beast the bunch.
They became good friends for hours –
Then he ate her up for lunch.

Claud

Claud cut himself up with a knife
To please his little nieces.
He lived a most unhappy life,
But now he'll rest in pieces.

Aunt Carol

Making vinegar, Aunt Carol
Fell into her brimming barrel.
As she drowned, my teardrops trickled;
Now she's permanently pickled.

Henrietta

Nature-loving Henrietta
Should have known a little better
Than to have continued reading
With an elephant stampeding.

Aunt Priscilla

Frail and fragile Aunt Priscilla
Wrestled with a wild gorilla,
And so savage was the winner
That she ate the ape for dinner.

Cousin Jane

Yesterday my cousin Jane
Said she was an aeroplane,
But I wanted further proof –
So I pushed her off the roof.

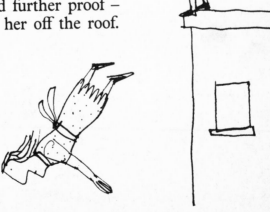

Myrtle

Falling from a window, Myrtle
To the ground began to hurtle.
As we watched her, Rodney reckoned
She reached forty feet per second.

NOTHING BUT NONSENSE

Orange Silver Sausage

Some words I've studied for a time,
Like *orange, silver, sausage*;
But as for finding them a rhyme,
I'm at a total lossage.

Brevity or
The Advantages of a Quick End

Should you hear a noise volcanic
And you see the earth erupt,
There will be no need to panic,
For your end will be abrupt.
Soon you'll feel the molten lava
As it swells around your feet,
But in places such as Java
There's no time to mind the heat.

Likewise, you should treat as petty
Any problems that arise
If you come across a Yeti
Who is over twice your size.
For he will not long detain you,
As your neck he tries to clutch;
In the seconds that remain, you
Won't have time to worry much!

Sir Hector

Sir Hector was a spectre
And he loved a lady ghost;
At midnight he'd collect her
And he'd drive her to the coast.

And there upon the shingle
They would rattle all their bones,
And ocean sounds would mingle
With their melancholy moans.

Stan

Before the camera
Stan's a stammerer,
So ill at ease
He can't say chhhh . . . .

85

Jocelyn, My Dragon

My dragon's name is Jocelyn,
He's something of a joke.
For Jocelyn is very tame,
He doesn't like to maul or maim,
Or breathe a fearsome fiery flame;
He's much too smart to smoke.

And when I take him to the park
The children form a queue,
And say, 'What lovely eyes of red!'
As one by one they pat his head.
And Jocelyn is so well-bred,
He only eats a few!

86

Pretty Polly Perkins

'Pretty Polly Perkins,
What would you like to eat?
Greengages and gherkins,
Or marmalade and meat?

Cakes and Coca Cola,
Or chocolate and ham?
Grapes and Gorgonzola,
Or sausages and jam?'

'Thank you, sir,' says Polly,
'But what would please me most
Would be a lemon lolly
Upon a slice of toast.'

Ladies First

The rule is always 'ladies first'
When passing through a doorway.
Throughout the world this rule applies,
From New Orleans to Norway.

And when about to go downstairs
Do *not* this rule abandon.
(Thus, should you ever chance to fall,
You've something soft to land on.)

Words with Teacher

These are the words that teachers use:
Hypothesis, hypotenuse,
Isosceles, trapezium,
Potassium, magnesium,
Denominator, catechism
And antidisestablishmentarianism.

I Used to Climb Up Lamp-posts, Sir

I used to climb up lamp-posts, sir,
At twelve o'clock at night.
I used to climb up lamp-posts, sir,
I knew it wasn't right.
I used to climb up lamp-posts, sir,
But now I've seen the light.

When Rover Passed Over

When Rover died, my sister cried;
I tried my best to calm her.
I said, 'We'll have him mummified,
I know a good embalmer.'

And so we packed the wretched pup
Into a wicker basket.
We duly had him bandaged up,
And kept him in a casket.

Now Rover we will not forget,
Though he is but a dummy.
For though we've lost a faithful pet,
We've gained an extra Mummy!

Inquisitiveness

Please, how does one spell *definite*?
Has it a double *f* in it?

Please, how old was Euripides?
And where are the Antipodes?

Please, what is a delphinium?
And whence comes aluminium?

Please, where does one find phosphorus?
And how big is the Bosporus?

Please, why are you so furious?
Do tell me, I'm *so* curious!

Don't Look in the Mirror, Maud

O, don't look in the mirror, Maud,
I fear that you might crack it.
A new one I could not afford,
Unless I sold my jacket.

And if I sold my jacket, Maud,
I could no longer wear it;
And then I couldn't go abroad –
I'm sure I couldn't bear it.

For if I couldn't travel, Maud,
I'd never go to Venice;
I'd have to stay behind with Claud,
And practise playing tennis.

And if he were to ask me, Maud,
If we could play mixed doubles,
He'd thereby contribute toward
My many other troubles.

For if we played mixed doubles, Maud,
With Vivian and Vera,
They'd dress me up just like a lord
Before that very mirror.

And if 'twere broke, they'd be appalled,
And hit me with my racket;
So don't look in the mirror, Maud,
I fear that you might crack it.

Geraldine Giraffe

The
longest
ever
woolly
scarf
was
worn
by
Geraldine
Giraffe.
Around
her
neck
the
scarf
she
wound,
but
still
it
trailed
upon
the
ground.

My Vulture

I once had a little vulture,
But he didn't care for culture,
And to let the whole world know it,
He would peck at any poet.
Though I begged him not to do so,
He would squawk all through Caruso,
And, what really seemed a scandal,
Hiccup all the way through Handel.
I once dragged him to a lecture
On Renaissance architecture,
But he found the subject boring
So he spent the whole time snoring.
When at last I took my vulture
To a show of modern sculpture
He just laughed at each exhibit –
So I hung him from a gibbet.

Still Life
with
Vulture

To Be a Bee?

To be a bee or not to be
A bee, that is the question.
You see, I'm in a quandary.
'To be a bee or not to be
A bee' is what perplexes me,
Pray, what is your suggestion?
To be a bee or not to be
A bee, that is the question.

The Height of Absurdity

I used to speak in Mexican
And travel by trapeze;
I used to practise Lexicon
With seven chimpanzees.

I used to bathe in turpentine
And play upon the flute;
I used to swim the Serpentine
Without a parachute.

I used to do so many things,
But that was long ago,
And now the thought of anything's
Abhorrent to me so.

The Wherefore and the Why

The Therefore and the Thereupon,
The Wherefore and the Why;
The Hitherto, the Whitherto,
The Thus, the Thence, the Thy.

The Whysoever, Whereupon,
The Whatsoever, Whence;
The Hereinafter, Hereupon,
The Herebefore and Hence.

The Thereby and the Thereabouts,
The Thee, the Thou, the Thine;
I don't care for their whereabouts,
And they don't care for mine!